More Music Reflections of Ir

25 of the very best Irish Songs & Dance Tunes, arranged for Guitar, Easy Piano, Keyboards, Harp, Accordion and Melody Instruments

selected and arranged by John Loesberg

harmonizations by Sarah Greenham

OSSIAN

part of The Music Sales Group

London / New York / Paris / Sydney / Copenhagen / Berlin / Madrid / Tokyo

Published by
Ossian Publications
8/9 Frith Street, London, W1D 3JB, UK.

Exclusive Distributors:
Music Sales Limited
Distribution Centre, Newmarket Road,
Bury St Edmunds, Suffolk, IP33 3YB, UK.

Music Sales Corporation
257 Park Avenue South, New York, NY10010
United States Of America.

Music Sales Pty Limited
120 Rothschild Avenue,
Rosebery, NSW 2018, Australia.

Order No. OMB43
ISBN 0-946005-37-0

Originally published in 1998.
This edition © Copyright 2005
Novello & Company Limited,
part of The Music Sales Group.

Special thanks to Sarah Greenham for her excellent
harmonies and Andrew Shiels for his typesetting.

Design & cover photograph by John Loesberg.

The words of some of the songs have been included
in this album. For complete versions of hundreds of
Irish songs, together with background notes see:

Folksongs and Ballads popular in Ireland Vols 1, 2, 3, 4
edited by John Loesberg (Ossian).

www.musicsales.com

A Bunch Of Thyme

Song

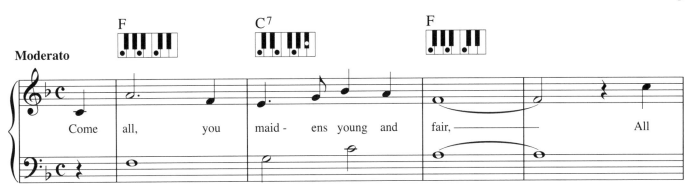

Moderato

Come all, you maid- ens young and fair, All

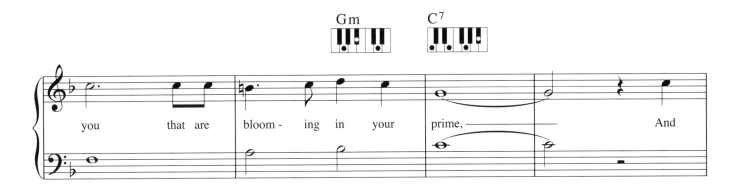

you that are bloom- ing in your prime, And

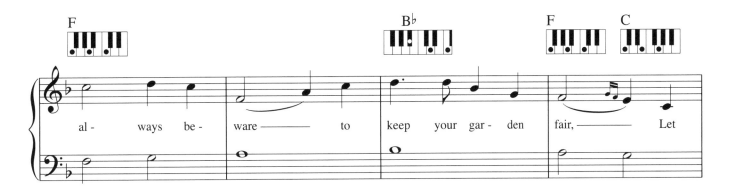

al- ways be- ware to keep your gar- den fair, Let

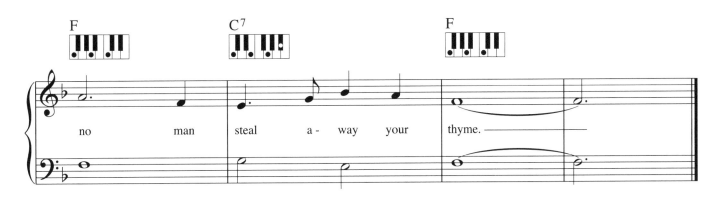

no man steal a- way your thyme.

Éireóidh Mé Amáireach

'Glenroe' Theme

Air

Fore, Co. Westmeath

The King Of The Fairies

Set Dance

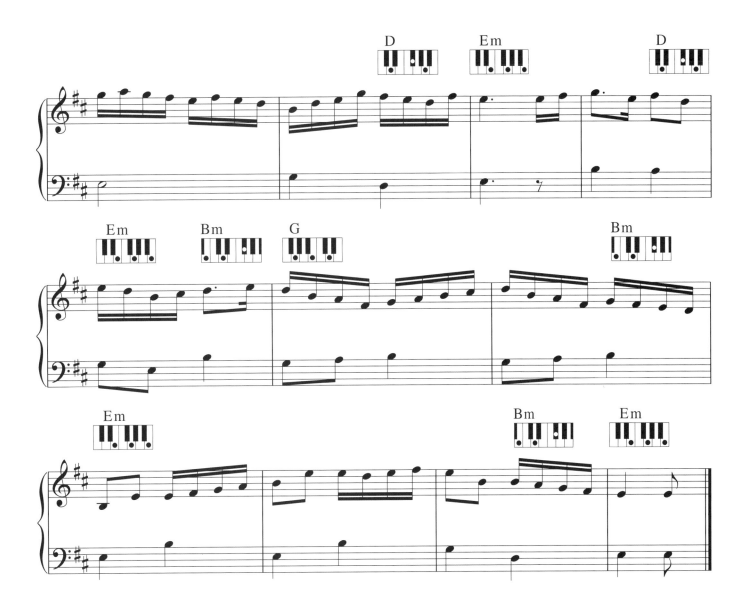

Stephen's Green, Dublin

Spancil hill

song

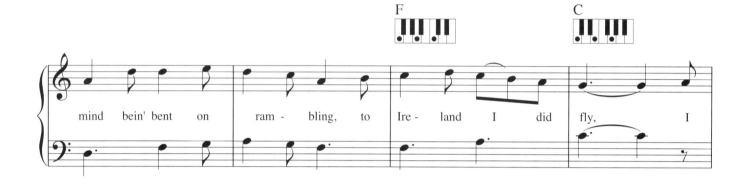

Last night as I lay dream- ing of plea- sant days gone by, Me

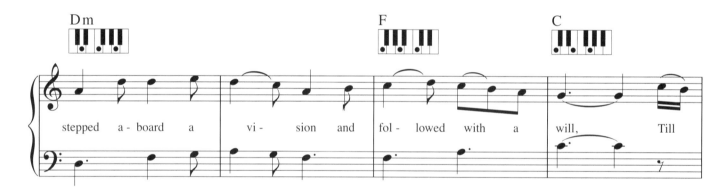

mind bein' bent on ram- bling, to Ire- land I did fly, I

stepped a- board a vi- sion and fol- lowed with a will, Till

next I came to anch- or at the cross near Span- cil Hill.

The Meeting Of The Waters

Air

Village on Achill Island

The Rose Of Mooncoin

Song

Oh! Molly, dear Molly, it breaks my fond heart
To know that we two for ever must part.
I'll think of you, Molly, while sun and moon shine
On the banks of the Suir that flows down by Mooncoin.
      Flow on lovely river etc.

She has sailed far away o'er the dark rolling foam
Far away from the hills of her dear Irish home
Where the fisherman sports with his boat and line
On the banks of the Suir that flows down by Mooncoin.
      Flow on lovely river etc.

Then here's to the Suir with its valleys so fair
As oft' time we wandered in the cool morning air
Where the roses are blooming and lilies entwine
On the banks of the Suir that flows down by Mooncoin
      Flow on lovely river etc.

Colonel John Irwin

O'Carolan (1670-1738)

She Moved Through the Fair

Song

13

Nora

Song

The vio- lets were scent- ing the woods, No- ra, dis-

play - ing their charm to the bee, When I first said I

loved on - ly you, No- ra, and you said you loved on - ly

me. The chest- nut blooms gleamed through the glade,

The golden-robed daffodils shone, Nora,
And danced in the breeze on the lea,
When I first said I loved only you Nora,
And you said you loved only me.

The trees, birds and bees sang a song, Nora,
Of happier transports to be.
When I first said I loved only you, Nora
And you said you loved only me.

A Kerry Polka

'Tis Pretty To Be In Ballinderry

Air

Cork Harbour

Spinningwheel Song

Song

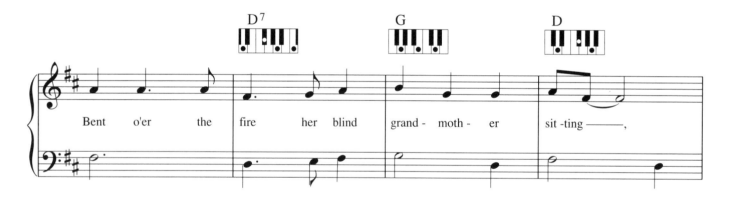

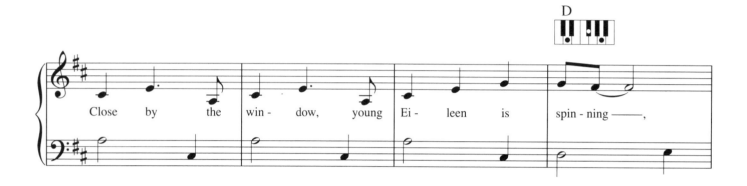

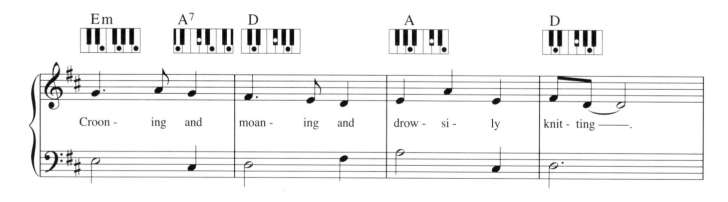

In Dublin's Fair City

Song

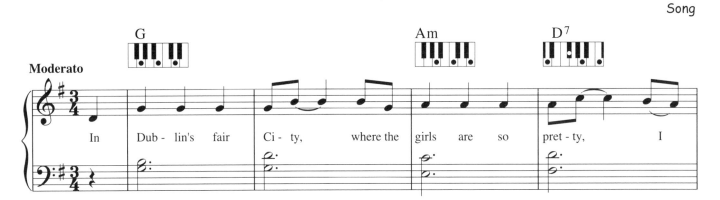

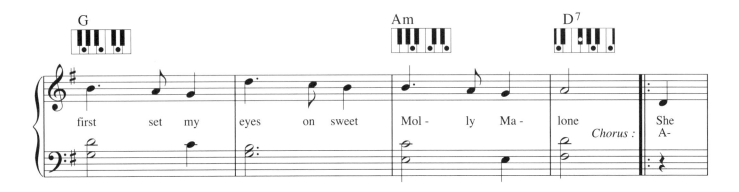

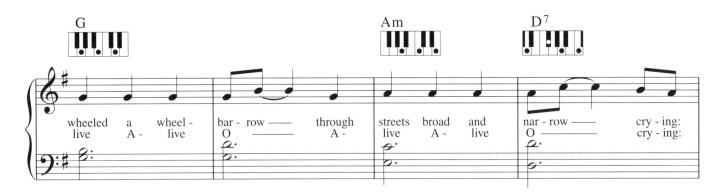

Blind Mary

O'Carolan (1670-1738)

Connemara Cradle Song

Song

Fanny Power

O'Carolan (1670-1738)

Oíche Nollag

(Christmas Eve)

Single Jig

24

The Wild Colonial Boy

Song

Mary From Dungloe

Song

The Wexford Carol

The Mountains Of Mourne

Song

Wellington's Advance

Double Jig

Suí Síos Fá Mo Dhídean

(Sit down under my protection)

Air

The Salamanca

Reel

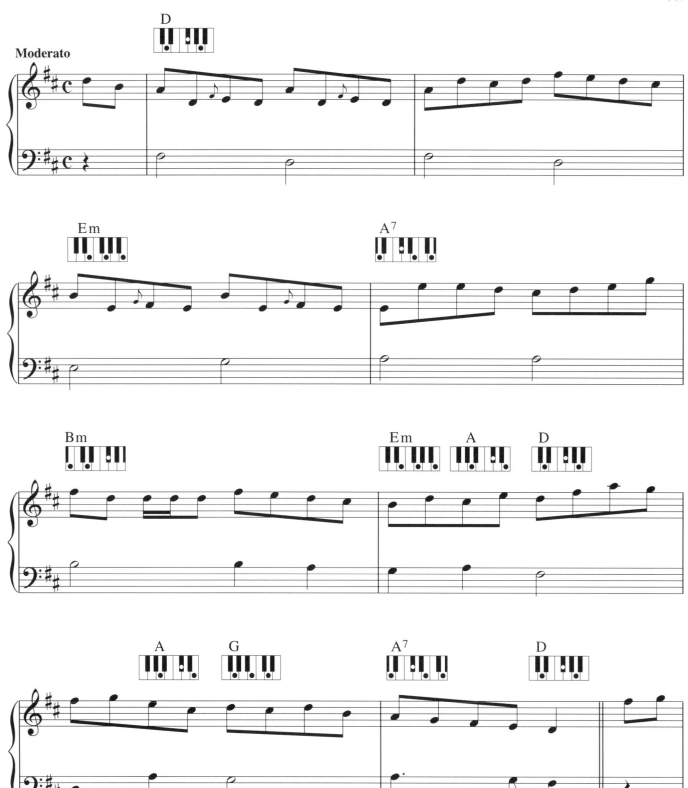

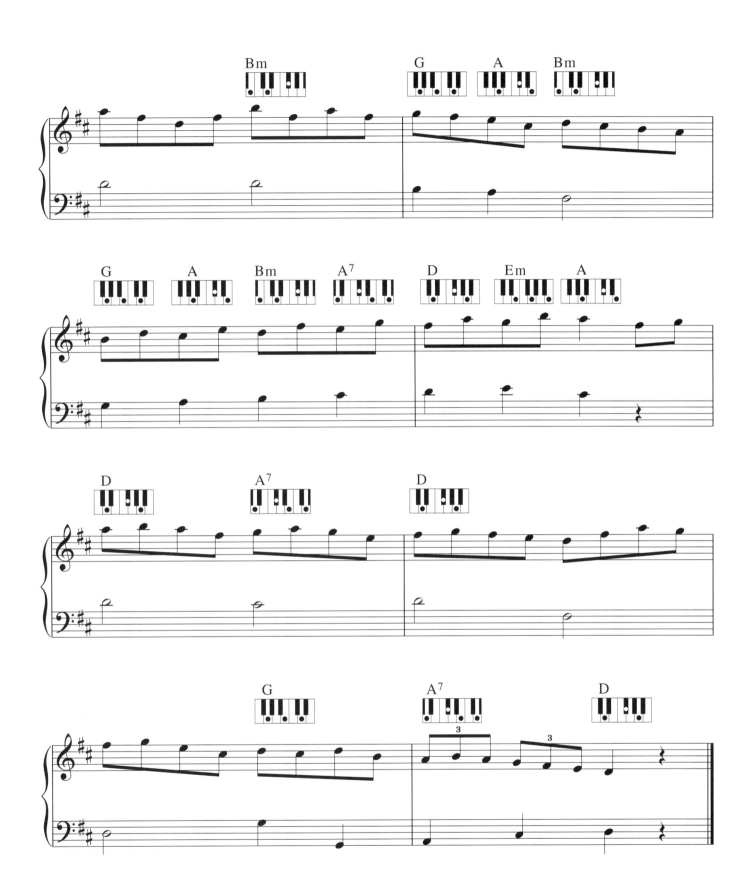

Come Back Paddy Reilly

Song

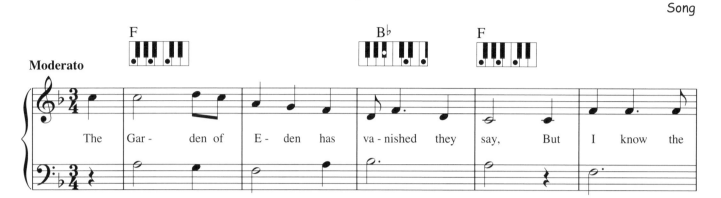

Moderato

The Gar - den of E - den has va - nished they say, But I know the

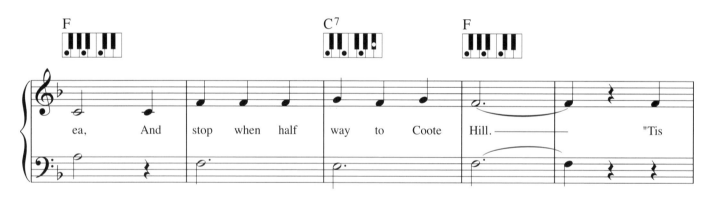

lie of it still. —— Just turn to the left at the bridge of Fin -

ea, And stop when half way to Coote Hill. —— "Tis

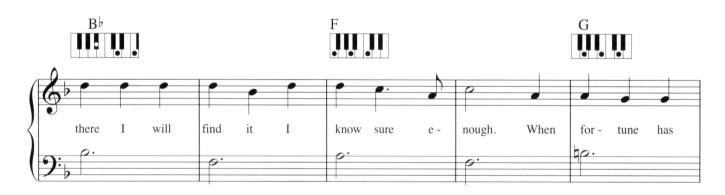

there I will find it I know sure e - nough. When for - tune has

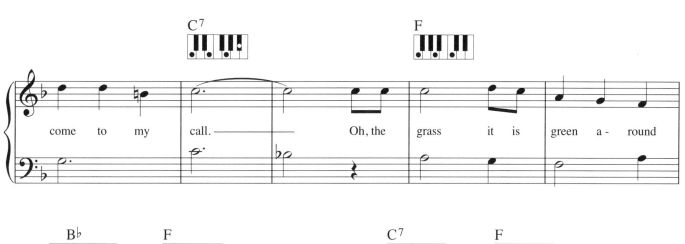

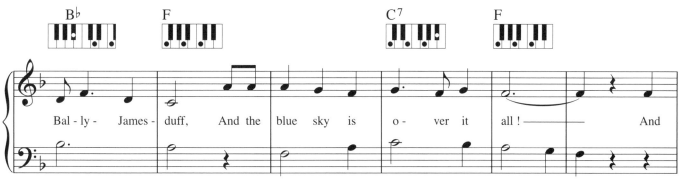

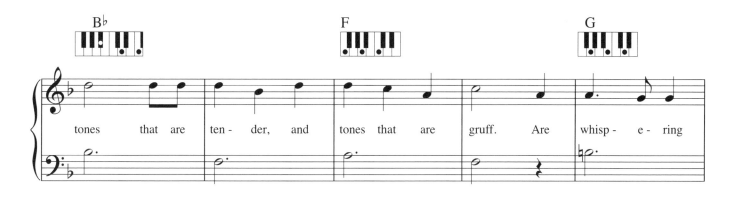

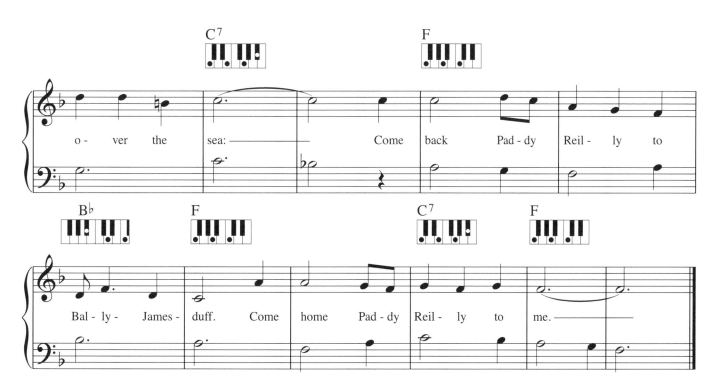